Big Fat Rat

Written by Nicola Sandford
Illustrated by Jess Mikhail

Rat hops on.
"Get off it, Rat."

Rat licks it.
"Less of it, Rat!"

Rat hops off.
Rat bobs up.

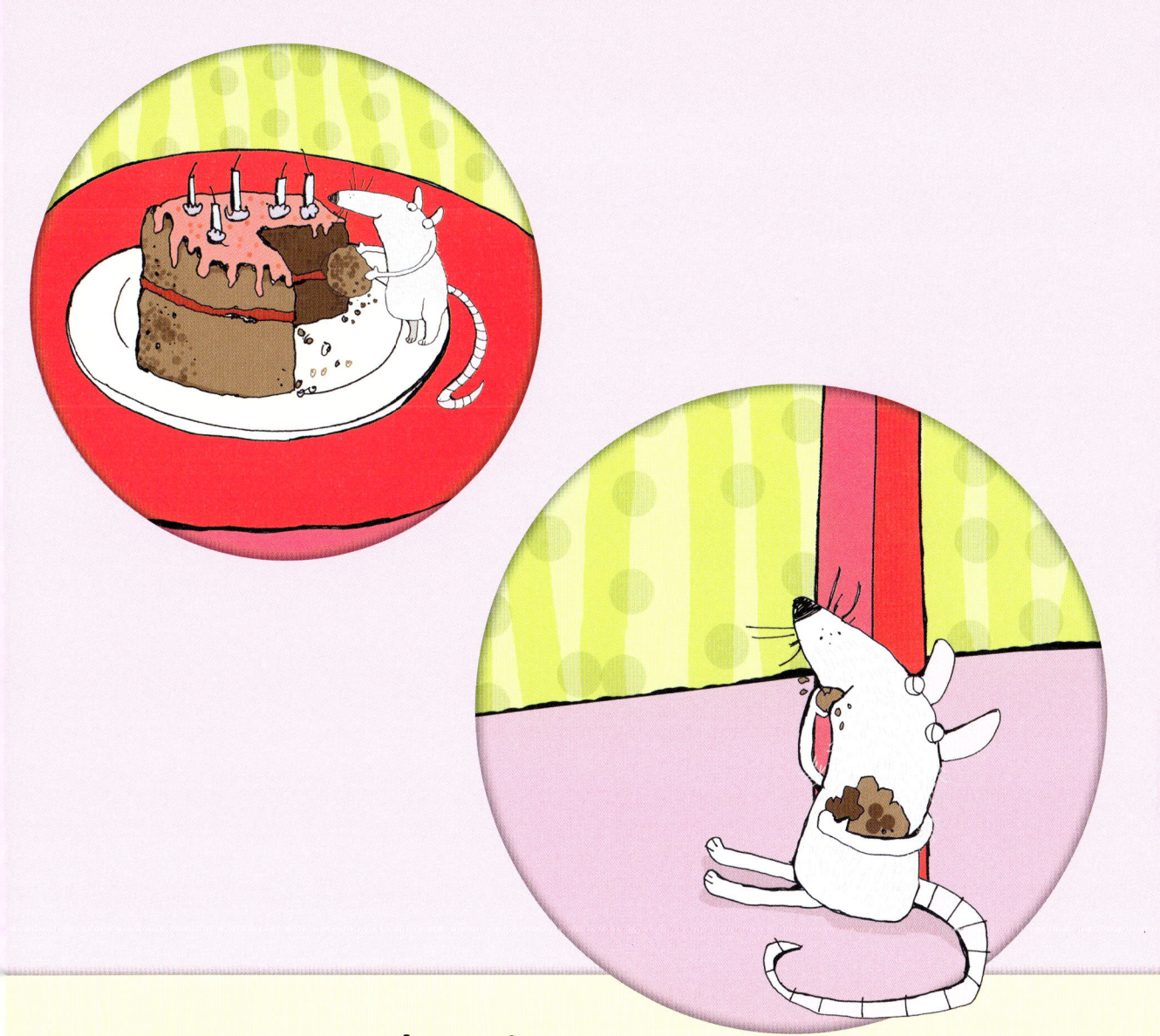

Rat tucks in.

Rat naps.
"I bet Rat is ill."

"Get into bed, Rat."

But Rat is not ill.
"Big fat Rat!"